Dot-to-Dots around the world

JO MOON

ARCTURUS

ARCTURUS

This edition published in 2019 by Arcturus Publishing Limited
26/27 Bickels Yard, 151–153 Bermondsey Street,
London SE1 3HA

Edited by JMS Books llp with Joe Harris & Jessica Sinyor
Layout by Chris Bell
Illustrations by Jo Moon

ISBN: 978-1-78428-535-7
CH005486NT
Supplier 29, Date 0919 Print run 9445

Printed in China

Off we go!

Let's join the dots to set off on our exciting journey around the world.

London

London is the capital of the United Kingdom.
A bus tour is a great way to see the city.

The Houses of Parliament have a famous clock.

Big Ben is the bell inside the clock tower.

Sahara Desert

This is the world's biggest desert.
It covers a large part of North Africa.

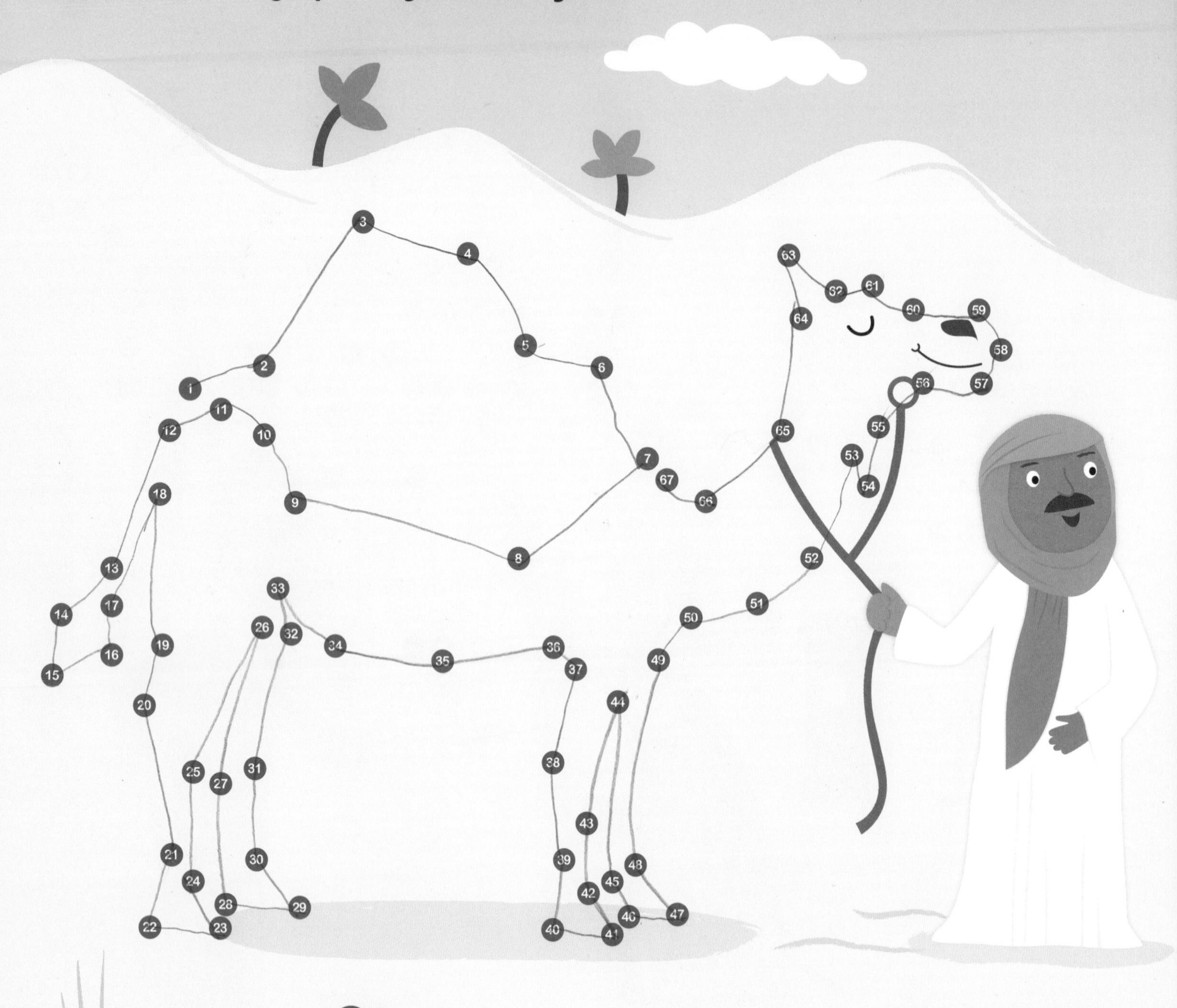

A camel with one hump is called a dromedary.
People who live in the desert keep cool inside large tents.

Pacific Ocean

This ocean is the biggest and deepest on Earth.

Sea turtles have two large flippers that look like paddles.
Blue whales are the largest animals ever known.

Egypt

This very dry country is famous for monuments built thousands of years ago.

The Ancient Egyptians built pyramids for pharaohs or rulers.

A mummy is a body that has been preserved after death.

Mount Everest

Mount Everest is the tallest mountain in the world.

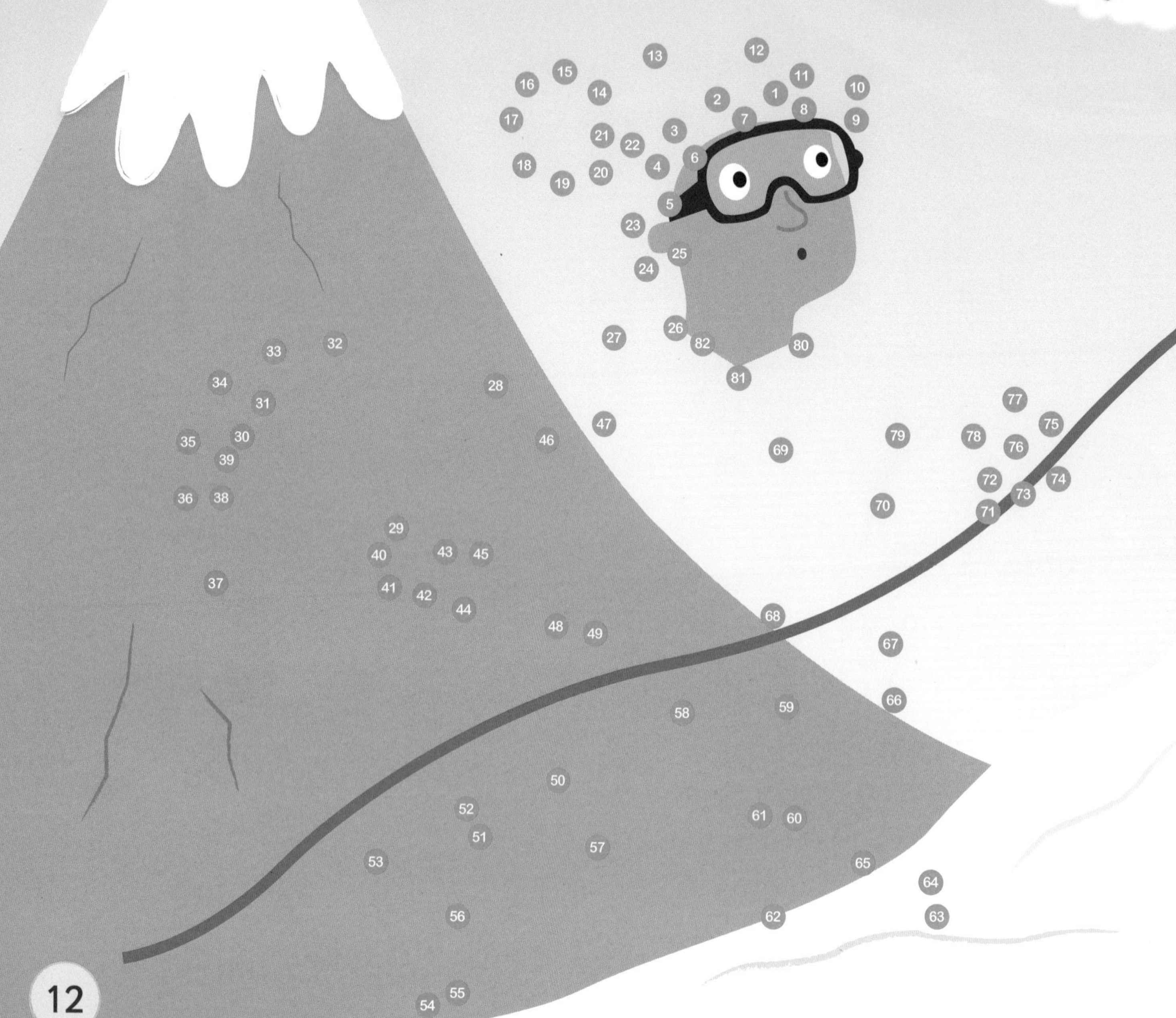

It is on the border between Nepal and China.
Local people believe that creatures called Yetis may live here.

Amazon Rain Forest

This rain forest in South America is the largest in the world.

A toucan's huge beak is called a bill.

Jaguars look like leopards, but are only found in the Americas.

35 34 33 31 32 36 30 37 38 43 29 28 39 42 44 40 27 41 45 46 3 47 54 2 4 26 63 1 49 51 14 15 56 58 57 59 13 6 12 7 17 24 8 11 10 9 18 20 21 19 23 22

Niagara Falls

These huge waterfalls are on the border between Canada and the United States.

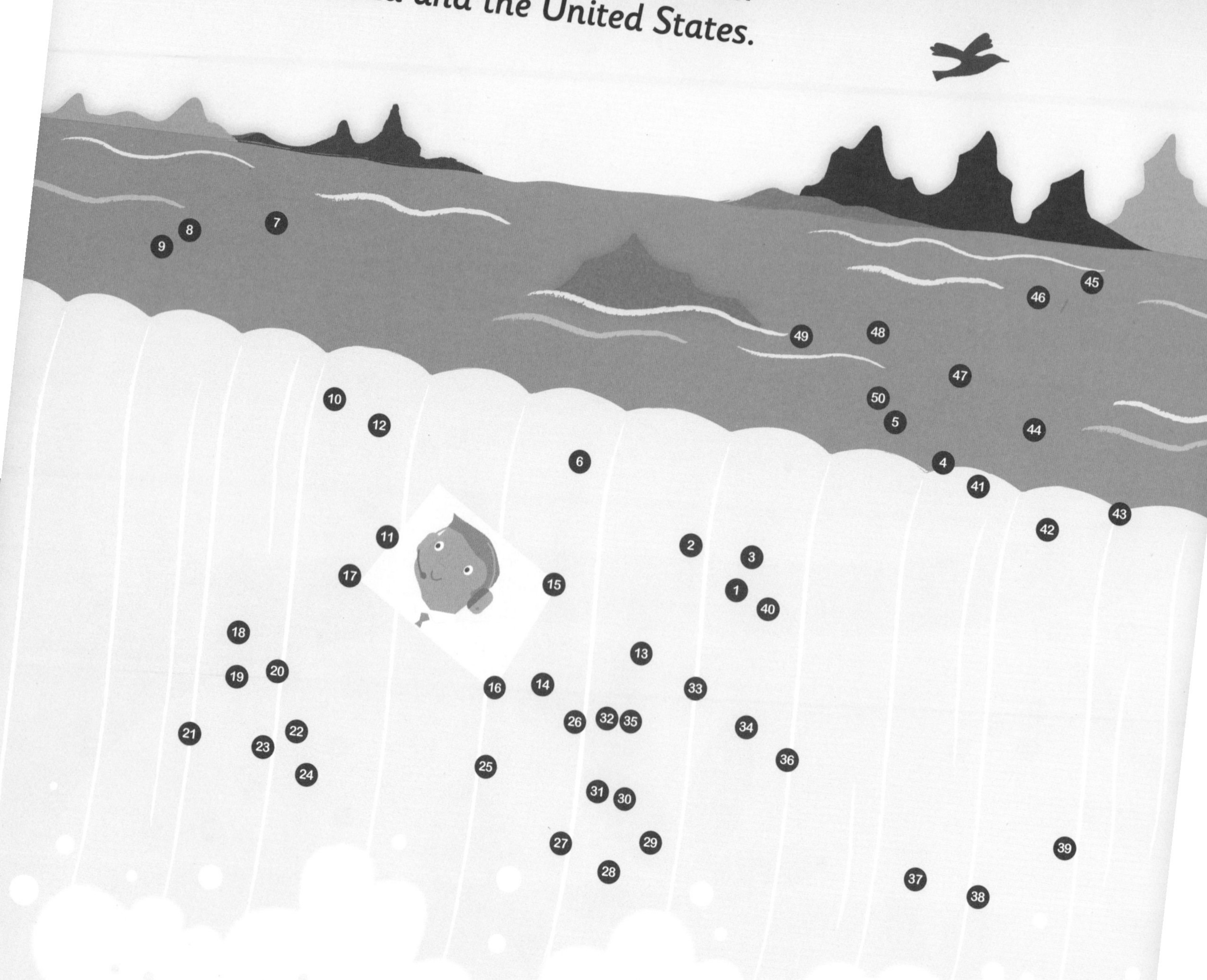

They are made up of three different waterfalls.
Brave people have walked across them on a high wire.

Pisa

Pisa is a city in Italy, with a very famous tower!

The Leaning Tower of Pisa leans to one side.

It was too heavy for the soft ground.

Moscow

Moscow is the capital of Russia and has a famous plaza called Red Square.

Cossacks kick their legs out when they dance.
St. Basil's Cathedral has lots of amazing patterns and shapes.

On Safari

The African plains are home to some wonderful wildlife.

A safari is a trip into the wild to see animals.
Only male lions have manes.

The Great Wall of China

Built by millions of people, this is the longest wall in the world!

The wall is more than 2,300 years old.

Giant pandas love to eat bamboo shoots.

Easter Island

Easter Island is a Polynesian island in the Pacific Ocean.

The island has around 900 giant human statues.

The islanders wear fantastic feather headdresses.

Uluru

Uluru is the name of a huge rock in Australia that is sacred to the Aborigines.

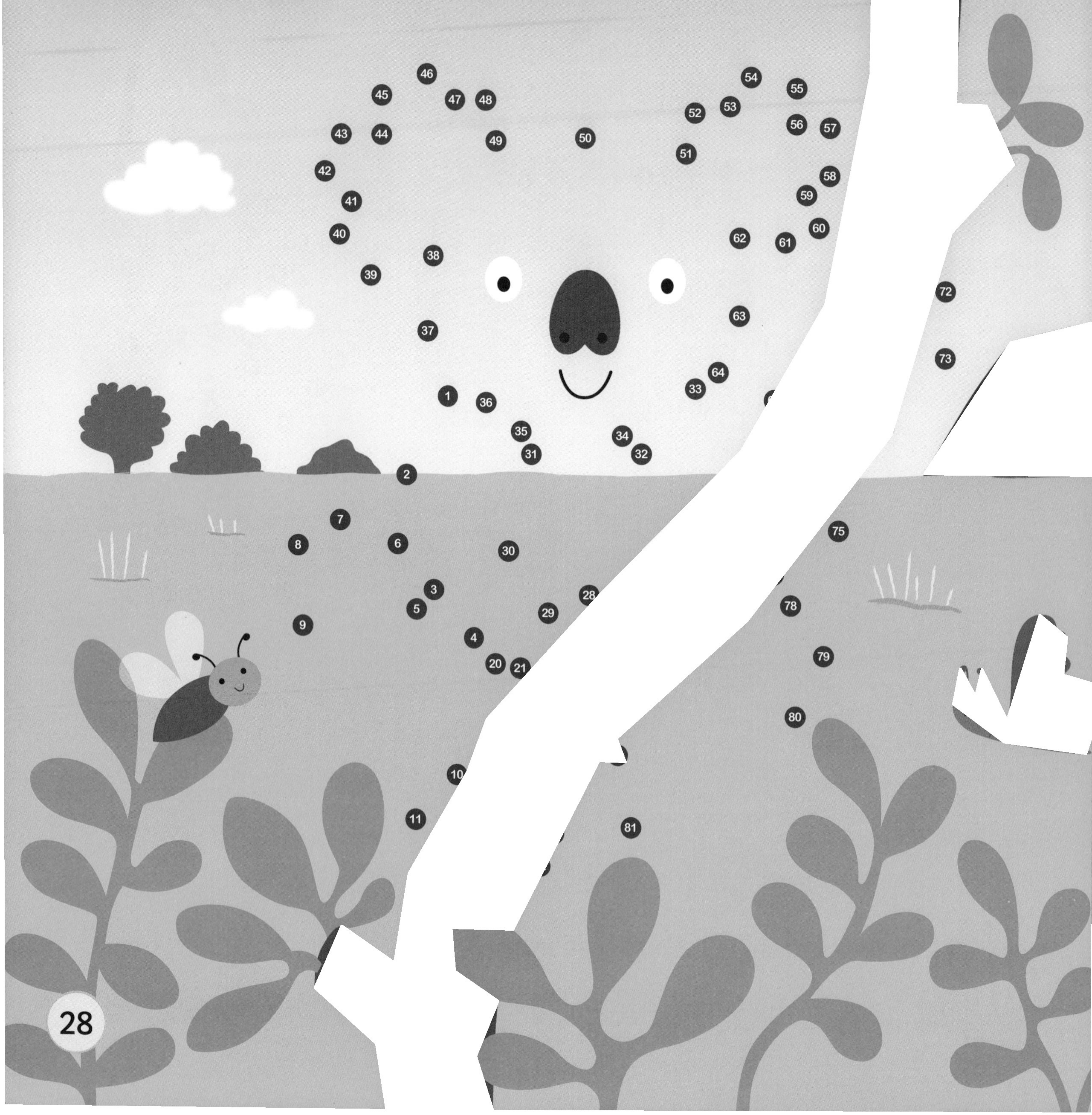

Koalas live in eucalyptus trees and eat the leaves.
The didgeridoo is a traditional musical instrument.

Mount Rushmore

This very famous monument in America was carved into the side of a mountain.

It took 400 stonemasons 14 years to finish the carving.
The faces belong to past American presidents.

Carnival in Rio!

Every year, Rio de Janeiro in Brazil is home to the biggest carnival in the world.

Over 2 million people visit the carnival each day.
People dress in amazing costumes and dance the samba.

The Taj Mahal

This white marble building is in India.
It was built in memory of Shah Jahan's wife.

The Colosseum

The Colosseum is in Rome, the capital of Italy, and was built by the Ancient Romans.

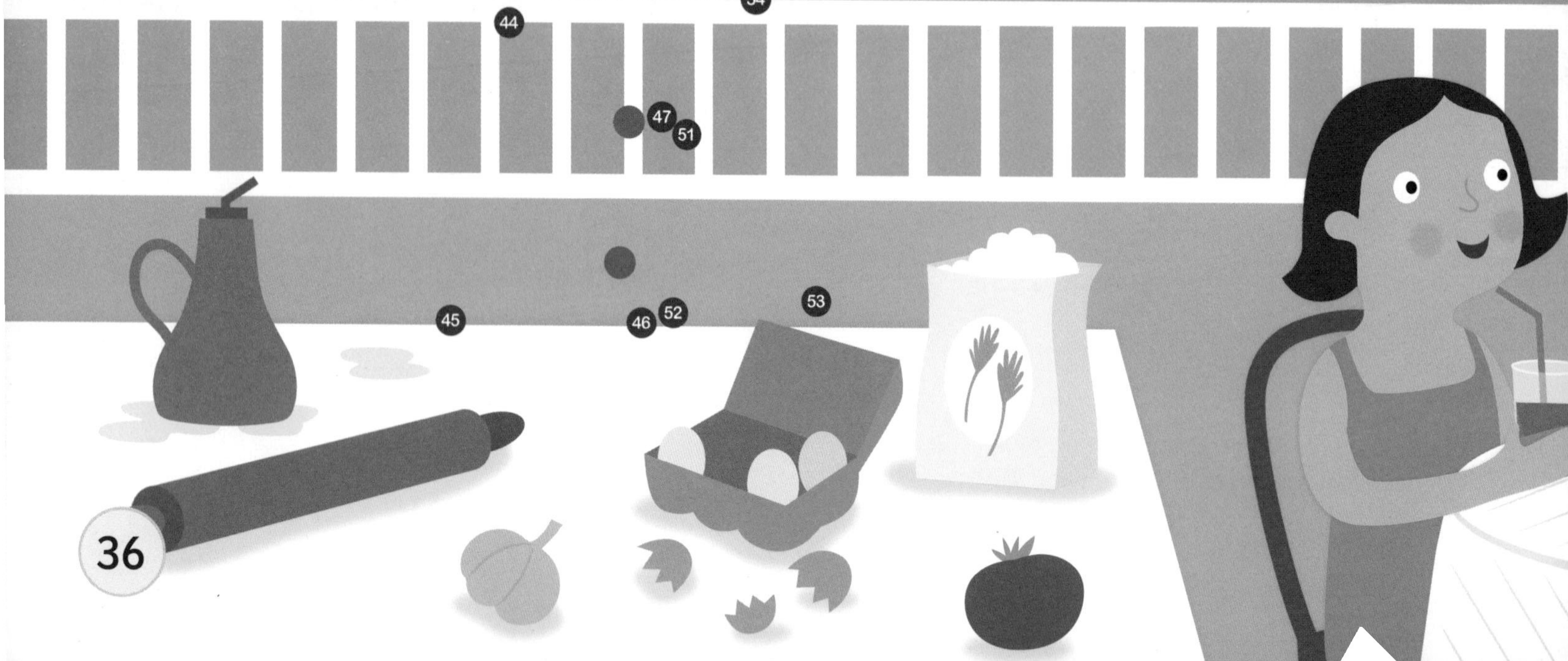

Gladiators used to fight in the Colosseum.
Italy is famous for its pizzas and pasta.

Mount Fuji

Mount Fuji is the highest mountain in Japan and is an active volcano.

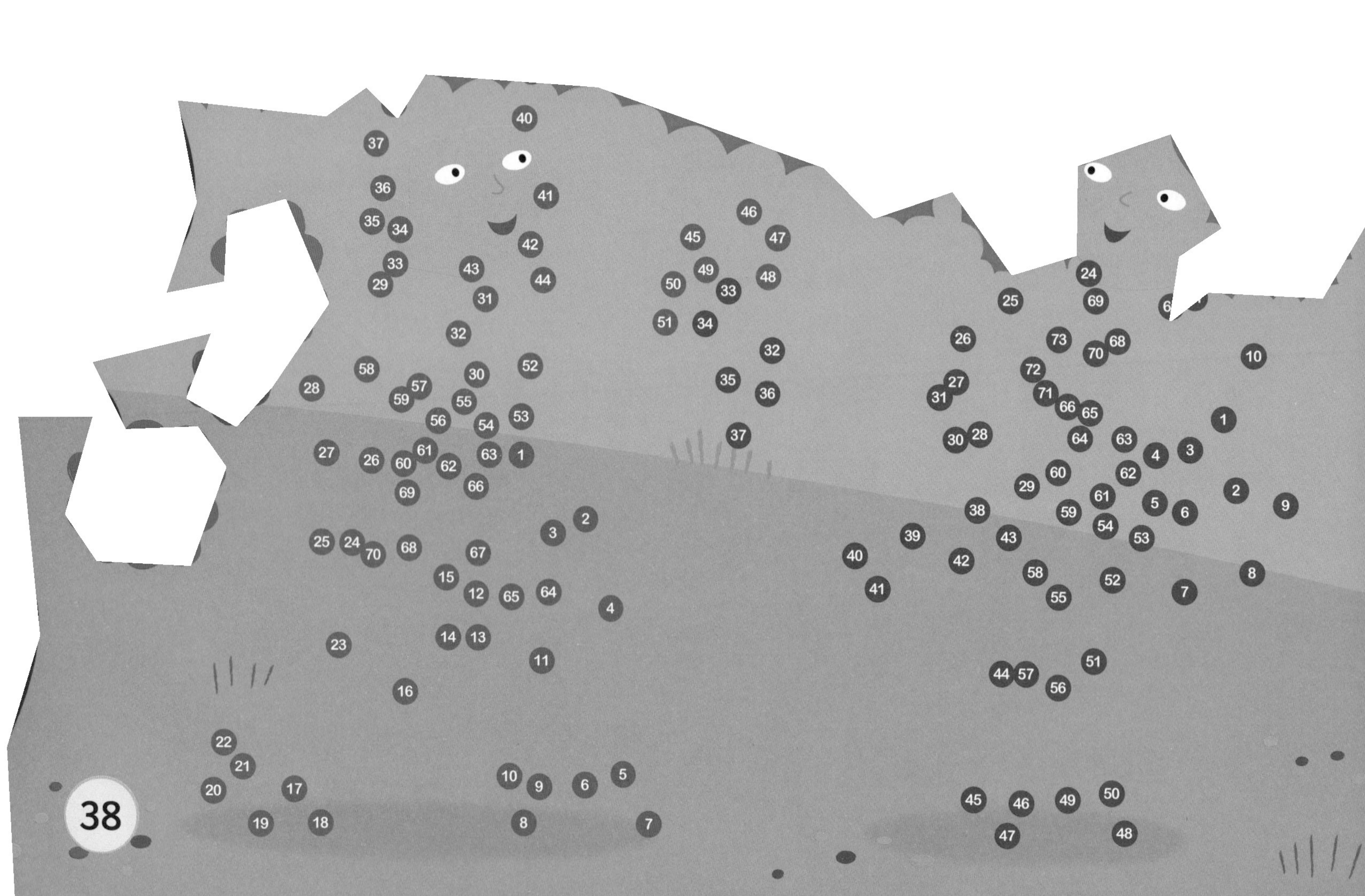

Karate is a sport in which you fight with your hands and your feet.
A pagoda is a building with lots of levels.

Mexico

Mexico City is the capital of Mexico and has a famous "Day of the Dead" festival.

People sing and dance to remember those who have died.
There are lots of skeleton puppets.

Brazil

Rio de Janeiro has long beaches and a very famous statue.

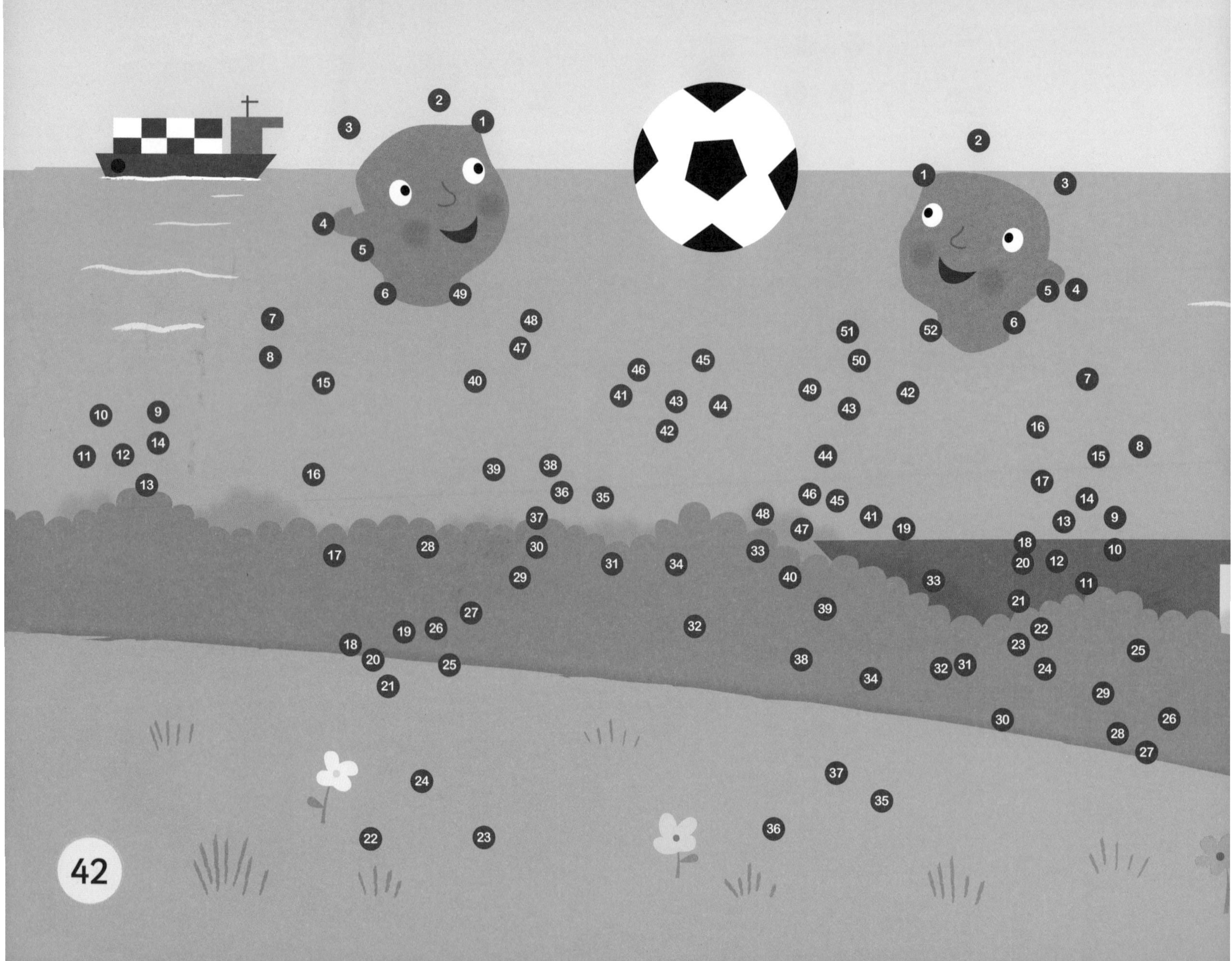

Brazilians play soccer wherever they can.
The statue, "Christ the Redeemer," towers over the city.

North Pole

The North Pole is in the Arctic and is the most northerly point on Earth.

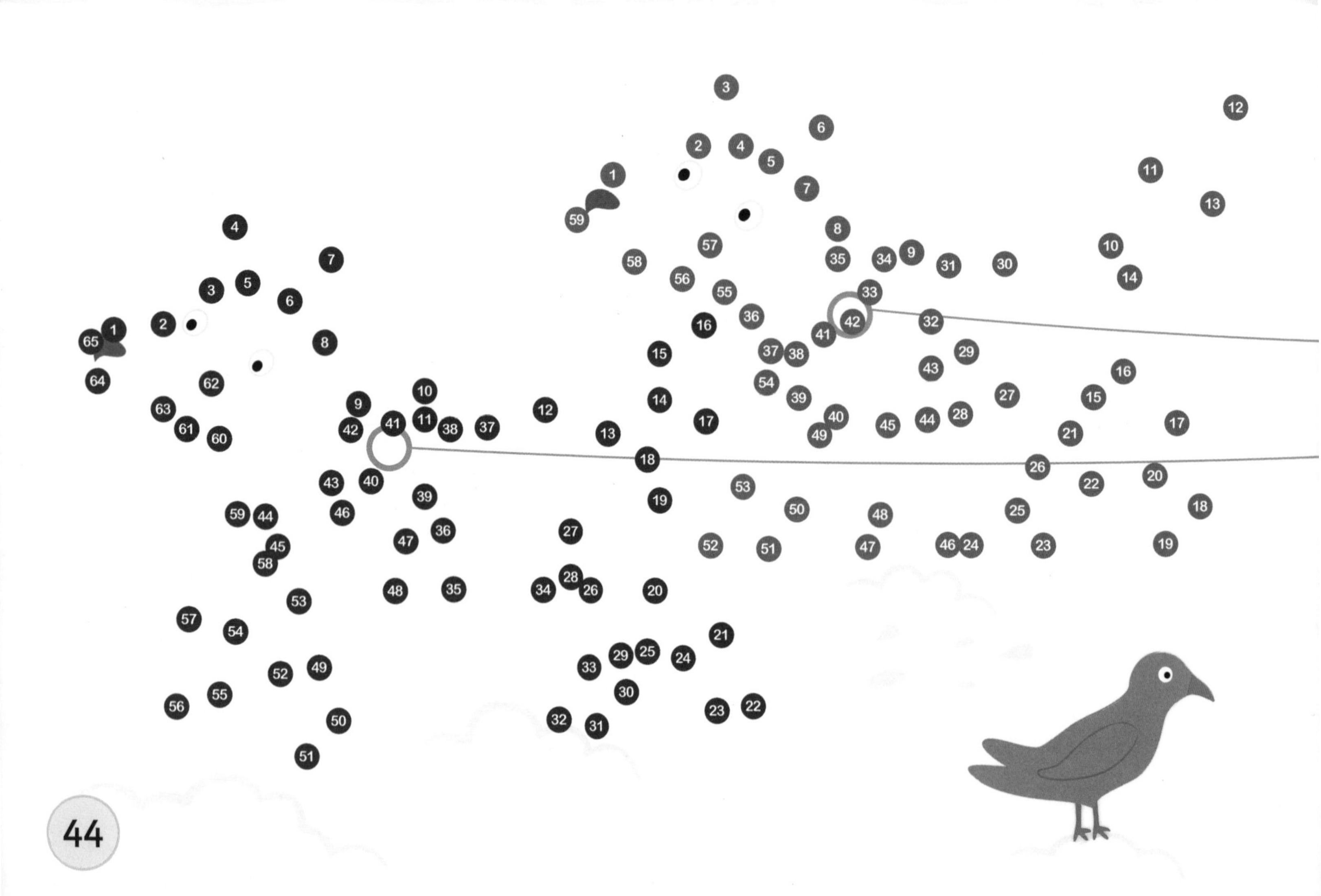

Polar bears live in the icy Arctic.

Huskies have a thick double coat of fur to keep warm.

South Pole

Seals have a layer of fat called blubber, for warmth.

Penguins cannot fly but are great swimmers.

The South Pole is in the Antarctic and is mostly covered in ice.

New York

New York is on the east coast of the United States and has lots of tall buildings called skyscrapers.

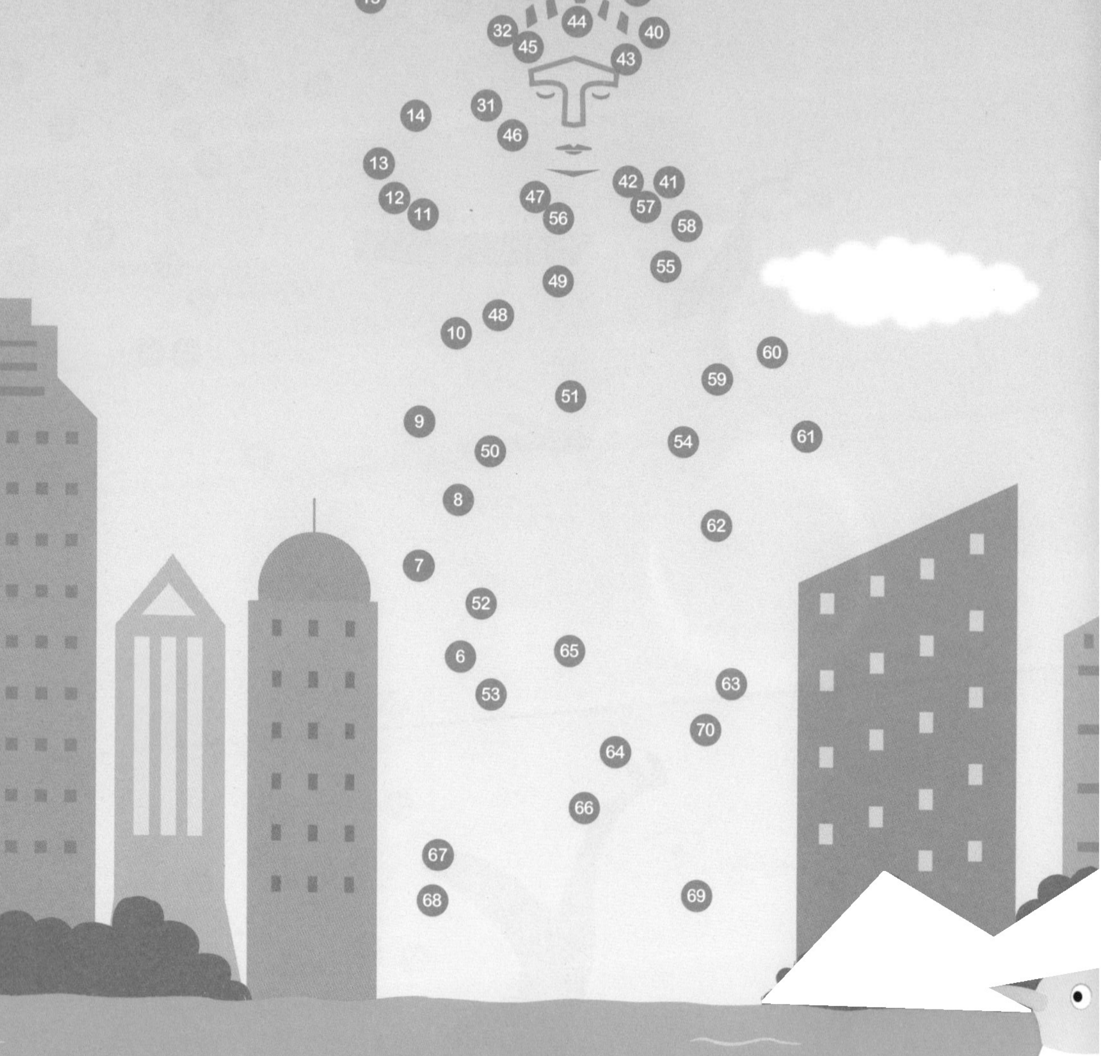

There are 354 steps in the Statue of Liberty.
The Empire State Building has 103 floors.

Cape Town

This sunny city is in South Africa and has long beaches and tall mountains.

Table Mountain has a flat top.
African porcupines have very strong claws.

Buckingham Palace

This is the London home of Queen Elizabeth II and her family.

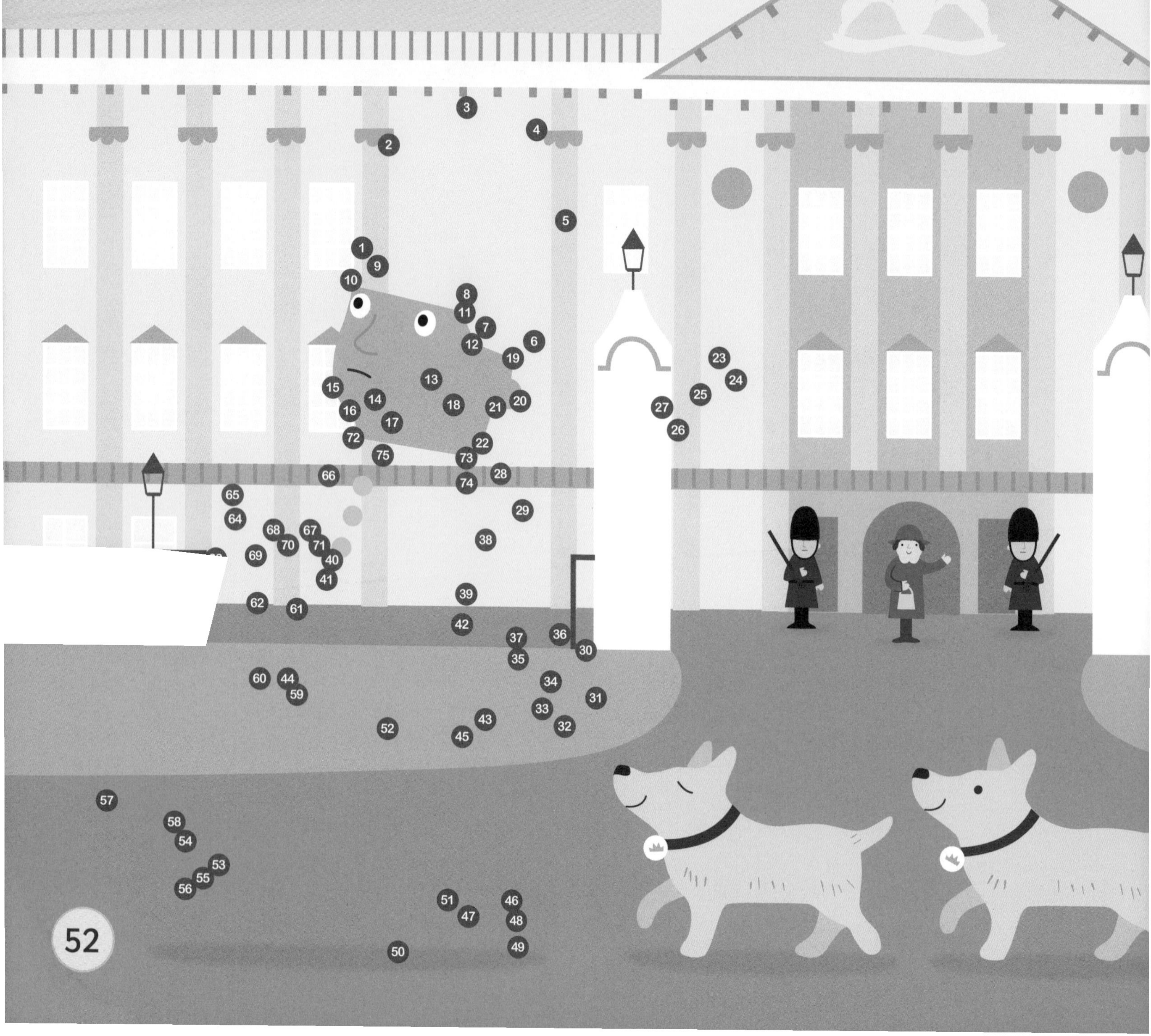

Millions of tourists come to see the palace every year.

The guardsmen wear tall fur hats called bearskins.

Cambodia

Angkor Wat is a large temple in Cambodia, Southeast Asia. It is surrounded by a moat.

African Savannah

The grasslands in Africa are called savannahs.
Lots of different animals live there.

Rhinoceroses have one or two horns.

Springboks are small antelopes that jump.

1 2 3 4 5 6 7 8 9 10 11 12 13 14 15 16 17 18 19 20 21 22 23 24 25 26 27 28 29 30 31 32 33 34 35 36 37 38 39 40 41 42 43 44 45 46 47 48 49 50 51 52 53 54 55 56 57 58 59 60 61 62 63 64 65 66 67 68 69 70 71 72 73 74

China

The Chinese New Year is celebrated with a big parade. It is also called the Spring Festival.

Some of the huge dragon costumes are made of paper.

There is lots of singing and dancing.

Paris

Paris is the capital of France. It is home to the Eiffel Tower and other well-known monuments.

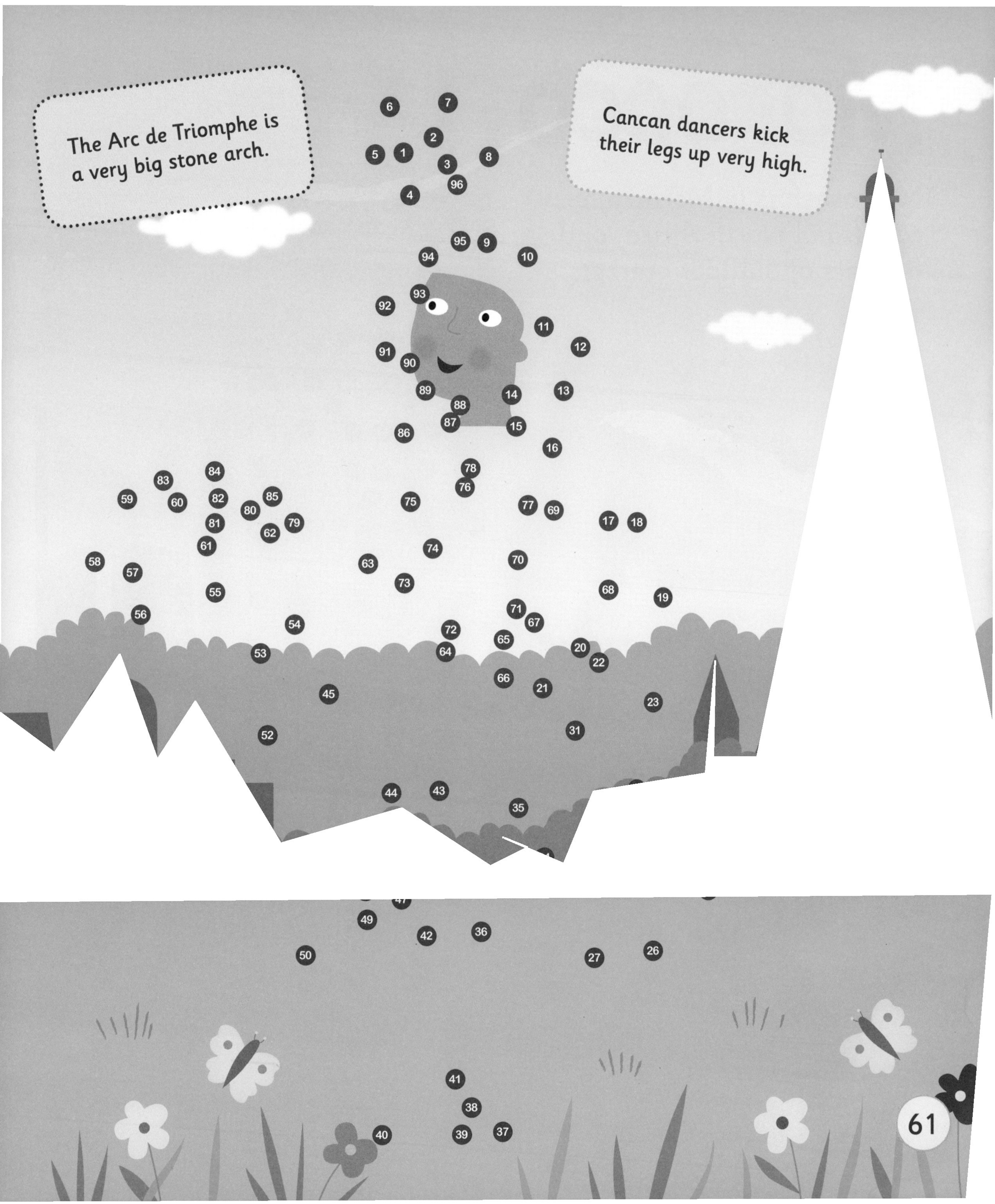
The Arc de Triomphe is a very big stone arch.
Cancan dancers kick their legs up very high.

Morocco

Marrakech is in Morocco, a country in North Africa, and has lots of outdoor markets.

The markets are called souks.

A minaret is the tower belonging to a mosque.

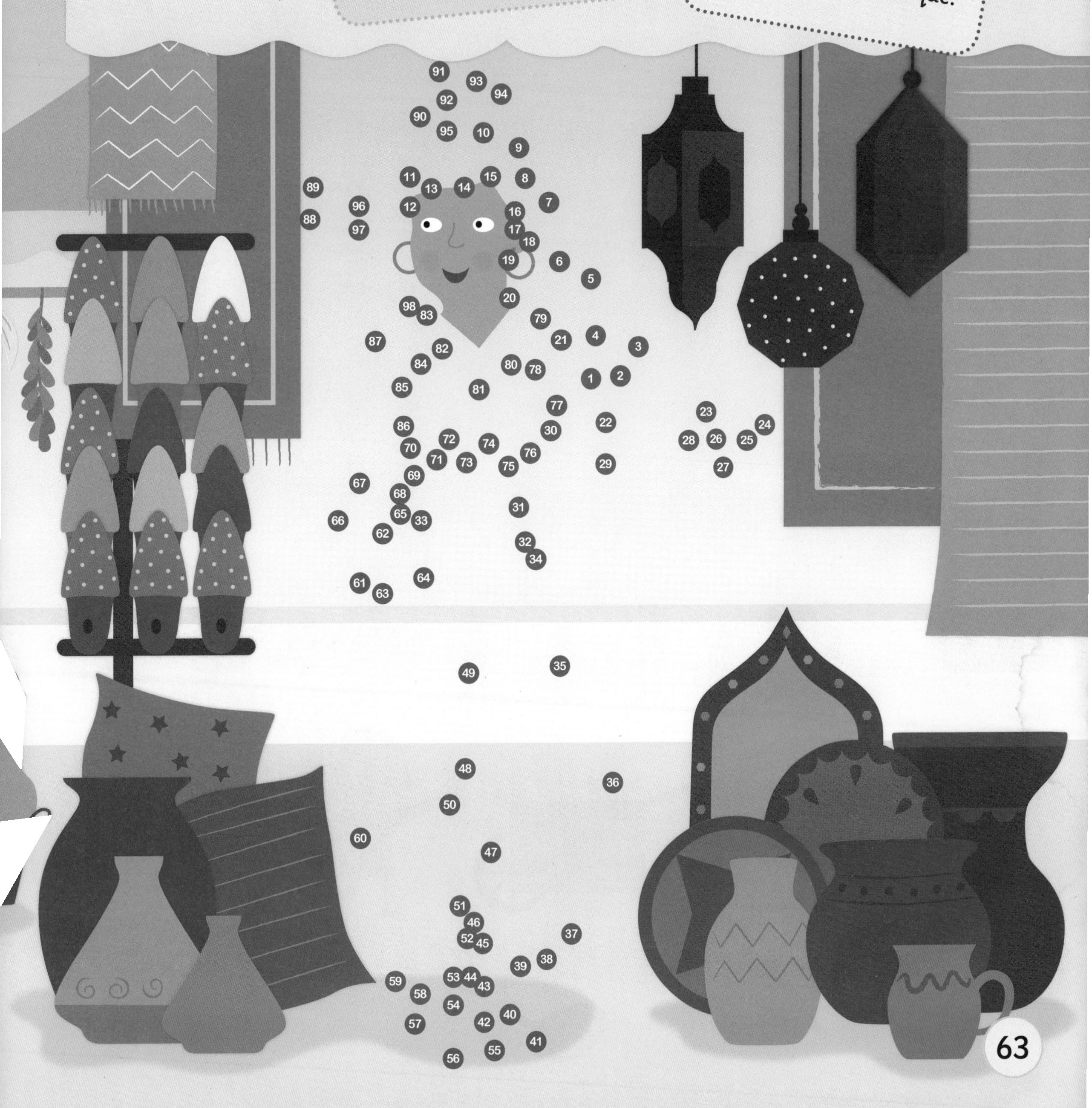

Berlin

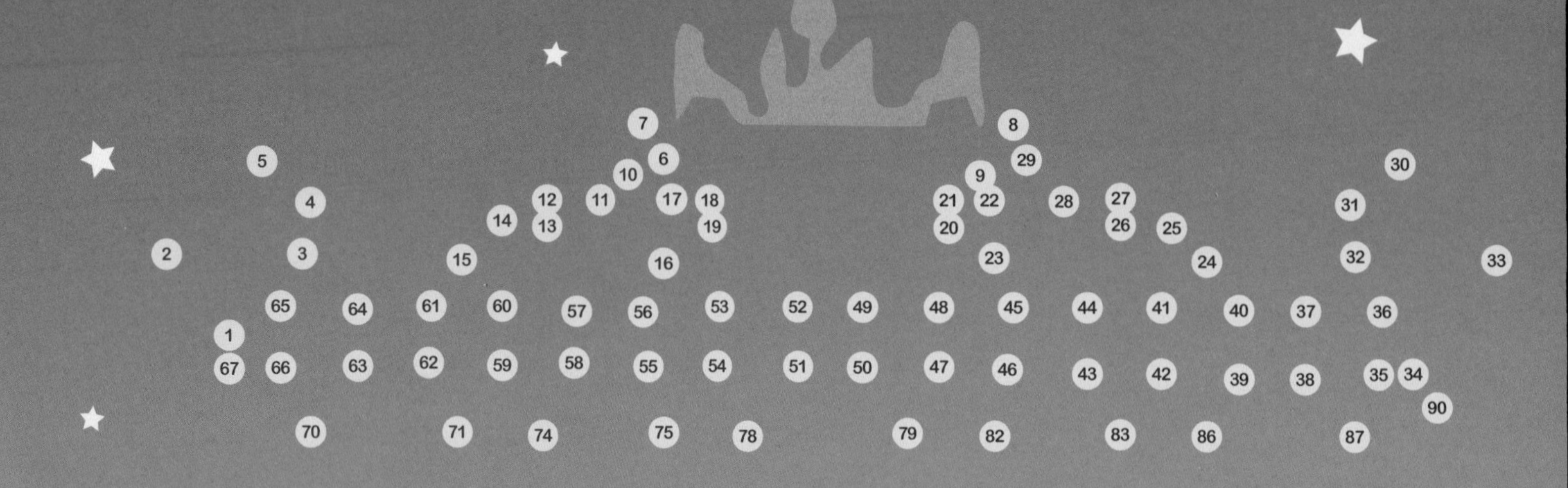

The historic Brandenburg Gate has 12 columns.

The Christmas markets sell tasty pretzels.

Hollywood

Hollywood is in Los Angeles in the United States and has its own very famous sign!

HOLLYWOOD

Movies and television shows are made here.

People take photos of the film stars.

38 39 17 18 35 37 40 16 41 19 34 15 33 20 36 42 14 21 12 13 22 43 45 44 32 46 49 11 23 24 31 10 30 50 47 9 29 48 25 27 8 28 51 7 6 26 4 3 5 52 2 1 54 61 62 53 60 55 63 70 56 57 59 58 69 65 64 68 66 67

Buenos Aires

This is the capital city of Argentina, South America, where people love to dance!

Tango dancers wear traditional dress.

An accordion player accompanies the dancers.

60 59 61 58 72 70 71 57 62 73 63 56 55 48 69 64 46 47 49 74 65 75 68 50 45 78 67 66 34 51 76 77 43 54 42 79 44 52 53 36 80 35 41 37 4 3 40 38 33 81 39 31 5 2 32 1 6 26 94 24 92 7 25 93 19 20 23 82 96 18 83 91 21 95 90 22 9 84 8 85 86 14 87 13 15 10 12 27 30 89 11 88 16 17 28 29

Diwali

Diwali is a very popular festival of lights in India, lasting five days!

People light candles and set off fireworks.
The beautiful temples are lit up at night.

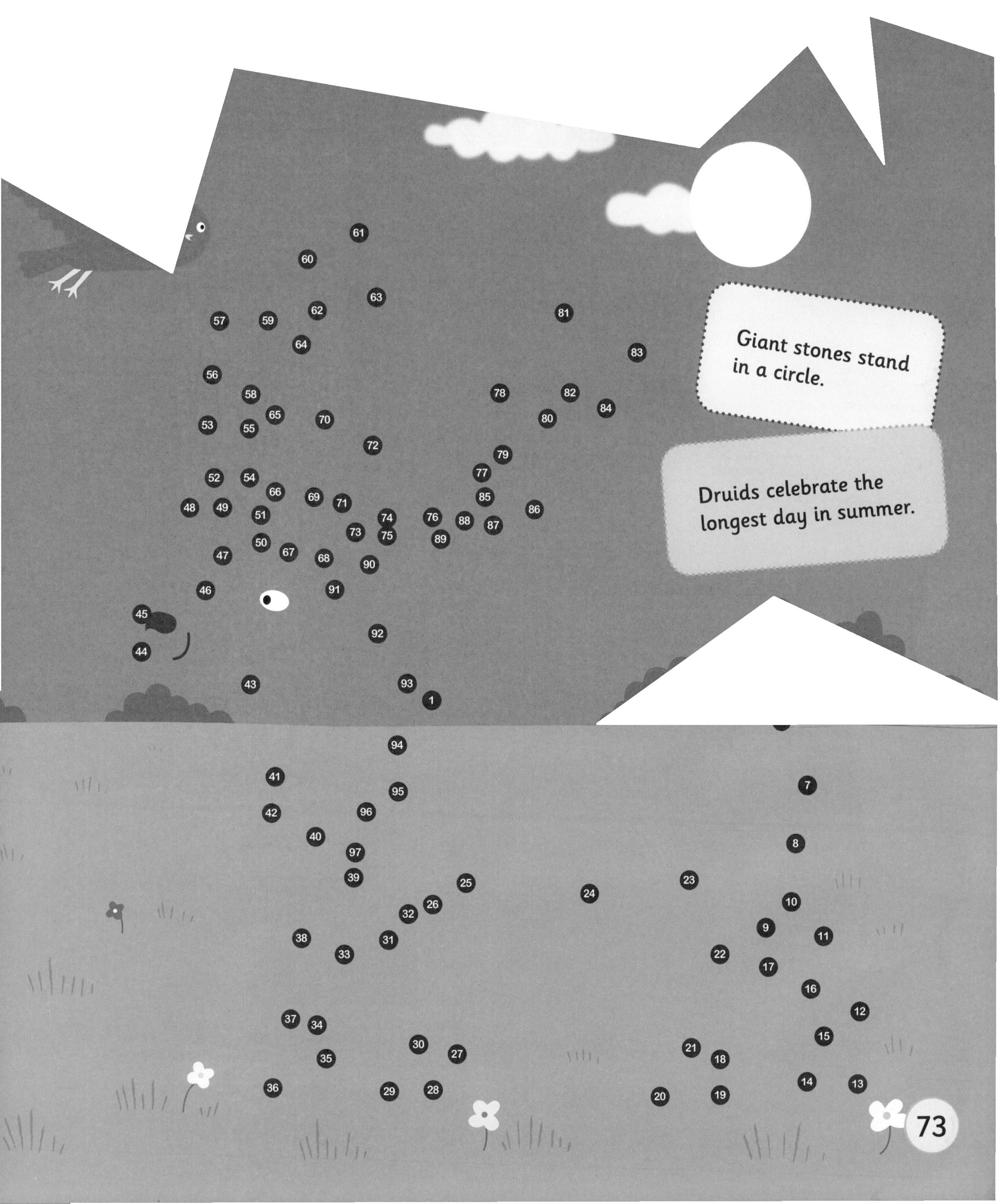
Giant stones stand in a circle.
Druids celebrate the longest day in summer.

San Francisco

This hilly city in the United States is famous for its Golden Gate Bridge.

The bridge is not golden but orange and red!

Cable cars carry people up steep hills.

Spain

People dance the flamenco during festivals and fiestas all over Spain.

Flamenco dancers wear traditional costume.
A guitarist plays music for the dancers.

Bavaria

In the state of Bavaria in Germany there is a fairytale castle built by a king.

King Ludwig lived in his palace for only six months.

Leather breeches, called Lederhosen, are traditional in Bavaria.

Chichen Itza

This ancient city in Mexico, with amazing pyramids, is one of the New Seven Wonders of the World.

It was built by the Mayans over 1,000 years ago.
Mexican children play with paper piñatas.

India

*People love to play cricket in India.
It is the number-one sport in the country.*

Cricket was first played here over 300 years ago.
Bowlers throw the ball and batsmen hit it.

Sydney

This Australian city is famous for its fabulous opera house. It looks like the sails of a ship.

Opera singers have very strong voices.

Fireworks are set off from the bridge at New Year.

Moose are members of the deer family.
The Canadian police are sometimes called Mounties.

St. Petersburg

This Russian city has a very famous cathedral and a beautiful Winter Palace.

"Matryoshkas" are Russian dolls that fit inside each other.
The dolls are usually in traditional dress.

Solutions

The following pages show you what was hidden in the pictures. Once you have joined the dots, your drawings should look just like these.

Page 3

Pages 4-5

Pages 6-7

Pages 8-9

Pages 10-11

Pages 12-13

Pages 14-15

Pages 16-17

Pages 18-19

Pages 20-21

Pages 22-23

Pages 24-25

Pages 26-27

Pages 28-29

Pages 30-31

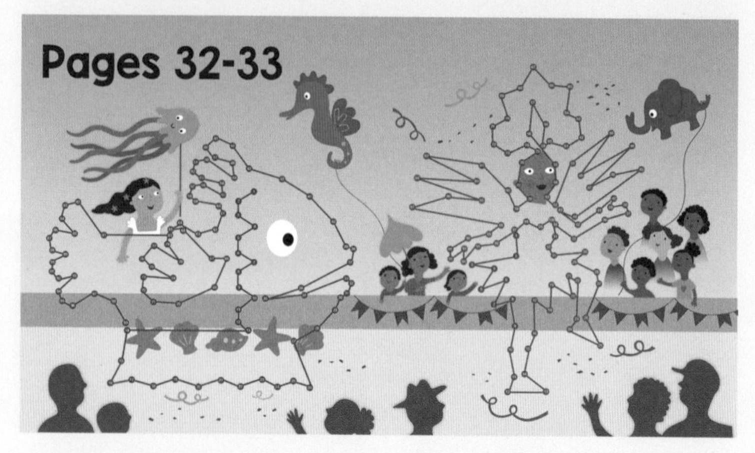
Pages 32-33

Pages 34-35

Pages 36-37

Pages 38-39

Pages 40-41

Pages 42-43

Pages 44-45

Pages 46-47

Pages
48-49

Pages 50-51

Pages 52-53

Pages 54-55

Pages 56-57

Pages 58-59

Pages 60-61

Pages 62-63

Pages 64-65

Pages 66-67
HOLLYWOOD

Pages 68-69

Pages 70-71

Pages 72-73

Pages 74-75

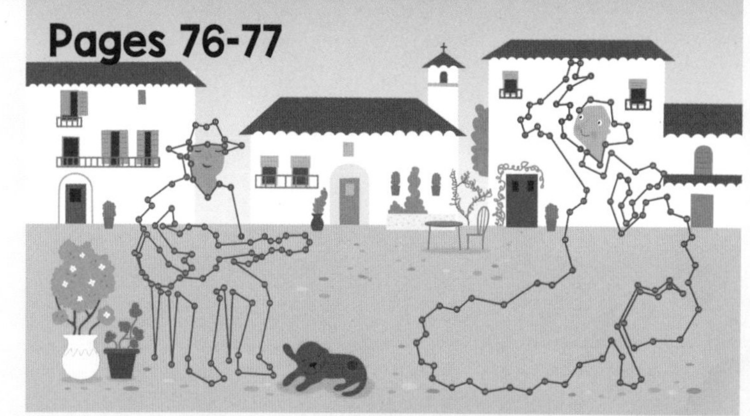
Pages 76-77

Pages 78-79

Pages 80-81

Pages 82-83

Pages 84-85

Pages 86-87

Pages 88-89

We hope you had fun on our dot-to-dot world tour!